M000097889

If You Tell Me,
I Can Fly!

Sharon Thayer

Illustrated by Linda Nagy

To Maelyn,
Believe and you will fly!

Sharon Thayer
2017

If You Tell Me, I Can Fly!

Written by Sharon Thayer
Illustrated by Linda Nagy
Scientific consulting by Tristan Kubik
Edited by Sharon Roe · www.SharonRoe.com
Graphic design by Hancey Design · www.HanceyDesign.com

Inquires should be sent to:
Carousel Publishing, Inc.
info@Carousel-Publishing.com
www.Carousel-Publishing.com

Cataloging-in-Publication Data
Thayer, Sharon
If You Tell Me, I Can Fly! (For Girls)
           p. cm.
1. Inspiration 2. Success 3. Young adult
I.Sharon Thayer II. If You Tell Me, I Can Fly!
ISBN 978-0-9766239-4-6
LCCN: 2016963112

Printed in the United States

This book is dedicated to those who see the strengths, visions, and dreams of others
and take time to give instruction, encouragement, and sometimes a little push
for the pure joy of watching them fly!

Thank You!

Winner of 7 Book Awards

If You Tell Me, I Can Fly! has been honored with:
- USA Best Book Gold Award
- Moonbeam Children's Book Bronze Award
- Eric Hoffer Award Finalist
- Four EVVY Awards from Colorado Independent Publishers Association

A special thank you to
Marlene Everson Roberts
for seeing my vision and for the push!

A caterpillar
inched along,
listening to a message:
a soft echo inside.

"I can fly!" she dreamed,
as she sunned her chrysalis,
and soon emerged a butterfly.

And she flew!

First exploring,
a baby hummingbird spied a hovering neighbor,
with such speed of beating wings.

"You can fly!" hummed his neighbor.
"What looks impossible is just not so.
Believe, and you can fly."

And he flew!

Only hours old,

a little bumblebee looked from his nest,
as the queen bee whispered,

"You can fly!
  With your heavy body and dainty wings,
    don't ask why—just fly!"

And he flew!

Upon a leaf,

a ladybug larva dreamed out loud,

"How I wish I could fly."

"You will soon fly.
Keep your dream alive and give it time,"
said a friend passing by.

And she flew!

An eaglet hops

back and forth across his nest.
His father calls as he soars by,
"Put your wings to the test.

You can fly!
   Take your first leap!
      I believe in you, now fly!"

And he flew!

A young woman emerges

from childhood's cocoon,
　　with dreams inside as big as the sky.

　　Alone at future's edge,
　　　　she glances back to her teachers,
　　　　family, and friends.

"If you tell me, I can fly..."

Author
Sharon Thayer

While growing up in the 1950s and '60s in Rockford, Illinois, we didn't have special education teachers who identified and worked with dyslexic students. At P.R. Walker Elementary School, as I awaited my turn to read aloud in class, I fought tears, my shaking hands, and the urge to run. No one ever explained my disability or taught skills to help me succeed.

My progression from a dyslexic, non-reading child to a national award-winning author was not one long successful flight, but many small ones where I gradually learned to focus on my strength of creativity. To compliment this strength, I surround myself with people whose skills in illustration, editing, and graphic arts have assisted in the successful flight of my books.

Today, as a full-time author, my hands don't shake, and I don't want to run. In fact, I look forward to reading aloud and sharing my stories while encouraging children to search for strengths as they prepare for amazing flights of their own.

If You Tell Me, I Can Fly! has been honored with the following awards:
  Eric Hoffer Award Finalist
  USA Best Book Gold Award
  Moonbeam Children's Book Bronze Award
  4 EVVY Book Awards from Colorado Independent Publishers Association

The Myth of Santa's Beard has been honored with the following book awards:
  Moonbeam Children's Book Bronze Award
  EVVY Bronze Book Award from Colorado Independent Publishers Association

Illustrator
Linda Nagy

Born in Atlanta, Georgia, Linda has been fascinated with art since childhood. She attended the University of Georgia where she earned BFA and MFA degrees in graphic design. Her career began at Hallmark Cards in Kansas City, Missouri, where she designed greeting cards in watercolor media.

Returning to Georgia, she worked for several years as a layout artist before establishing a retail and direct marketing business with her husband, Bernie. In their time off, they traveled extensively throughout the US, Europe, South America, and New Zealand, as Linda's eclectic style constantly evolved, reflecting new techniques and influences. The rich tapestry of events in Linda's life has influenced her art, but color is the dominant feature that permeates all her works.

Now retired in South Park, Colorado, Linda and Bernie write and publish Colorado nature books. Their latest project, published in 2014, is *Rocky Mountain Wildflowers Field Guide*.

Colorado's South Park: High Country Paradise, has been honored with the following awards:
   EVVY Award from Colorado Independent Publishers Association
   International Book Awards

South Park, Colorado: Nature's Paradise has been honored with the following awards:
   3 EVVY Awards plus the Past President's Award from Colorado Independent
      Publishers Association

Scientific Animal Facts

The animals in this book were chosen because of their unique way of becoming creatures of flight.
Below are facts about how each comes to fly.
I wish you luck in discovering your own unique way to fly!
– Sharon Thayer

Hummingbird:
Mature hummingbirds beat their wings 12-80 times per second, while their hearts beat 12 times per second. To sustain this behavior, they require a nectar-rich diet in addition to a healthy number of insects.

Butterfly:
When a caterpillar sheds its skin, it becomes a chrysalis. Within the chrysalis, the original body converts into a protein soup, and not even the brain or heart survive this transformation. Slowly the soup is rearranged into a butterfly, which then breaks its way out of the chrysalis. After pumping blood into its wings, it flies.

Bumblebee:
Most insects that have rapid wing flight, like the bumblebee, move their wings in a rotation pattern. This pattern works with the wind. A conventional flap, like that of a bird, works against the wind. This rapid wing flight motion saves a lot of energy for the insect and allows heavier weight to be lifted per wing surface area.

Ladybug Beetle:
Ladybug beetle larvae survive only if they can avoid ant threats and feast on aphids. This aphid feast occurs for several weeks, and then the larva pupates. The pupa grows wings and the ability to fly, and therefore can escape from the ants as an adult ladybug beetle.

Eagle:
Eaglets are fed vigorously for the first month or so in preparation for their fledgling flight. The eaglets can practice flapping their wings by hopping from branch to branch or across the nest, but the first departure from the nest is the final test. Either they fly or fall to their death.

Carousel Publishing's mission is to produce products with quality-of-life messages for all ages. Outlined below are some of the ways we assure our books and messages find their way into hands and hearts.

Author Programs: Sharon is available for readings, signings, speeches and workshops. Topics include:

- And She Flew! Sharon's Inspirational Story
- Eight Ways to Create Traditions for Stronger Families
- Tactics for Teaching Strengths and Weaknesses in Your Classroom
- A Billion Benefits for Kids Who Plug into Nature
- Explore the Features and Facets of Journaling (Adult program and student program)
- How to Build a Stupendous Story! (For elementary school children)
- Is Santa Claus Real? - Answering the inevitable question (For adult audiences)

Fundraising & Donation Programs:

Often, those who most need a special story or an inspirational message are not in a place where they will receive such a gift. Carousel Publishing works with individuals and corporations in gifting books and raising funds for nonprofit organizations.

In the past, we have helped raise funds or gifted books to children at Ronald McDonald Houses, Toys for Tots, Girl Scouts, Big Brothers Big Sisters, as well as shelters, hospitals, and schools. Please share your goals and we will help you succeed.

For additional information go to Book Signings & Programs at www.Carousel-Publishing.com or email Sharon@Carousel-Publishing.com to reserve your date!